maegical
Tails

Pepe's Grounding Adventure

Written by Maegen and David Staab   Illustrated by Cameron Villanueva

Little Pepe woke up with great joy in his heart,

For today was the day his first adventure would start!

Pepe loved learning lessons and gaining helpful skills,

He would also get to collect a relic, oh what a thrill!

2

He walked downstairs and was greeted by his mom with a big hug,

"You look so cute my Pepe, like a snug bug in a rug!"

His dad belly laughed and said when he was done,

"Just do the best you can my son, and don't forget to have fun!"

Pepe began walking through the Land of Gratitude on the crystal path,

For he knew if he followed it closely, he would make it to Maegical Mountain at last!

The crystal path was surrounded by stones that glimmered and gleaned,

They shined beautifully in the sun, but Pepe barely noticed their sheen.

5

Welcome to
THE LAND
OF GRATITUDE

6

Pepe was so excited he ran all the way to the end,

He didn't stop once, he didn't even notice he passed his friend!

He saw the bottom of the mountain and he couldn't hold it in any longer,

He screamed "Waaahhoooo I have never felt stronger!"

7

Maegical Mountain looked majestic and wild animals were all about,

This was different from his homeland, where only pets lived throughout!

But these weren't just wild animals- they were a special sort,

They were master teachers of life skills as the legends report.

11

Pepe was in awe of the beauty of the mountain,

There were large trees and bushes, natural waterfalls and fountains!

He knew the legends of the master teachers in the wild,

He thought to himself "I'm ready lets do this!" and started hiking with a smile.

Pepe hiked long and hard with a pep in his step,

He knew it wasn't going to be easy- this he did accept,

But as the day grew longer, doubt crept in his mind,

"What if I can't do this, what If this teacher I never find?"

14

He started to get discouraged and slowed down his pace,

Then all of a sudden he heard a powerful voice that lit up his face!

"You are strong, healthy and you can do anything you put your mind to,

Now put your chin up, think a positive thought and know it to be true!"

Pepe listened to the words and knew this voice was right

He immediately felt better and lit up like a light!

"Thank you kind sir, may I ask where you are?"

"I'm ten feet behind you, you blew past me from afar!"

18

Pepe looked back behind him and there was quite the sight,

A stocky looking turtle glowing forest green that was so bright!

"It's great to see you Pepe my friend,

Come on over here, have a seat and listen in!"

Pepe was starstruck but excited all the same,

He went and sat down, and was so happy he had came.

"I'm ready for my skill- I'll learn it right now!

I'm so very excited sir- let's get started tell me how!"

"The skill you must learn will be of more value than you know,

While you may not be aware there is a powerful change you must undergo.

I love your excitement, you've been this eager for what it's worth,

But there is great power in being present and taking time to connect with the earth."

24

This was new to little Pepe, he was always excitable and go go go,

"How do I do this Great Turtle, I truly want to know!"

"Walk over here with me my child, to this clearing that I found,

The forest ranger cleared the area of any dangers on the ground."

"Take off your shoes, take a slow deep breath, allow your feet to feel the earth.

Think about only this moment right here and now, understand its priceless worth."

As Pepe began to do this all his sense kicked into gear like never before,

He noticed the true beauty around him, felt extreme gratitude and relaxed even more!

Pepe saw the beauty in the bushes, each leaf with a custom design,

He could hear the waterfall behind the trees, and smell the scent of fresh pine.

He felt no worry, felt no stress, just felt alive and perfect right then and there,

He could sense and feel everything around him from the dirt up to the air.

30

"Grounding daily in nature can be quite profound,

The smells, the sights, overall connection to nature and the sounds.

It can help you relax, feel peace, and appreciate each and every moment,

You can do it anytime you are outside, it is our most important daily component."

Pepe felt connected to nature like he had never been before.

He was overwhelmed with gratitude, and filled with love even more.

Then all of the sudden both his feet began to glow forest green,

Pepe's eyes grew wide as he looked down, it was quiet the scene!

"That's your relic for acquiring the skill young one,

You have learned the lesson, now it's time to have fun!

Anytime you ground yourself, your feet will practically glow,

Your feet are like antennae that recieve nature's electric flow"

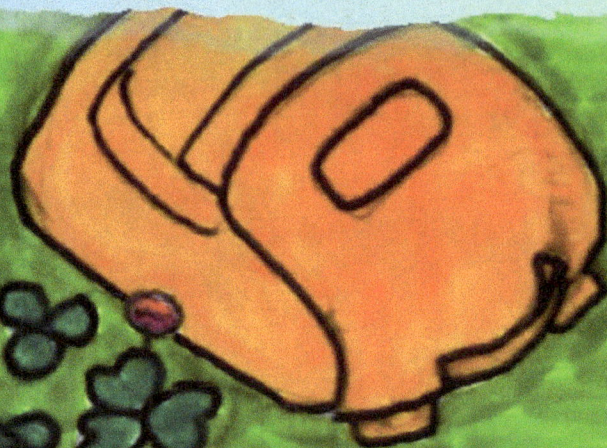

Pepe was so grateful for the lesson, it was exactly what he needed,

He would start doing grounding walks more often, as Great Turtle had heeded.

Living more in the moment, not rushing to get here or there,

Enjoying life's moments one by one, not dwelling on worries or snares.

"Thank you so very much Great Turtle, I am grateful for your gift.

I will take it to heart and use it daily, I can already feel a shift."

Pepe started back home from the mountain waiving Great Turtle goodbye,

He knew he learned such a valuable lesson, that he could not deny.

40

This time when Pepe got off the mountain and stumbled upon The Crystal Path,

He found a safe space and grounded himself, and gave his paws a dirt bath.

His feet lit up green and he could feel the connection quick,

He was relaxed, peaceful, and much calmer, this was the best mood to pick!

Instead of running this time, he walked back to his home, noticing everything around,

He noticed all the different colors of the crystals, the smell of flowers were abound,

He even stopped to talk to his friend that he passed so fast on his way up,

They had a wonderful conversation, Pepe was feeling like a brand new pup!

Pepe got home, crawled into bed, and reflected deeply on the day.

He was full of gratitude, full of love, and smiled while he laid.

At least one time a day he would let his feet glow forest green,

A trick so essential to living a life most serene.